The Mystery at Number Seven, Rue Petite

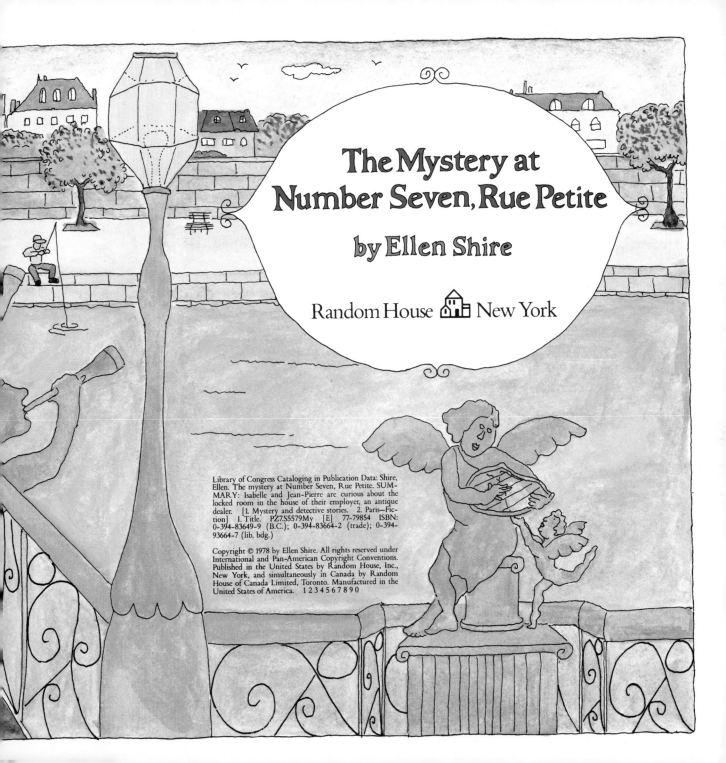

The Mystery at Number Seven, Rue Petite

by Ellen Shire

Random House New York

Library of Congress Cataloging in Publication Data: Shire, Ellen. The mystery at Number Seven, Rue Petite. SUMMARY: Isabelle and Jean-Pierre are curious about the locked room in the house of their employer, an antique dealer. [1. Mystery and detective stories. 2. Paris—Fiction] I. Title. PZ7.S5579My [E] 77-79854 ISBN: 0-394-83649-9 (B.C.); 0-394-83664-2 (trade); 0-394-93664-7 (lib. bdg.)

MONSIEUR POMPEUX
ANTIQUAIRE

In the city of Paris, the day always began early at number seven, Rue Petite.

"Bonjour," said Isabelle, the housekeeper, as she threw open the shutters on the top floor and started to clean.

"Bonjour," answered her husband, Jean-Pierre, as he began to prepare the day's meals in the kitchen below.

But Monsieur Pompeux just grumbled to himself as he opened his antique shop on the ground floor of his house.

Soon the store was full of customers. People came from all over to bargain and buy at number seven, Rue Petite. This made Monsieur Pompeux very rich and it should have made him happy. But nothing could make Monsieur Pompeux happy. He never smiled, not even at his best customers. He just grunted and took their money.

Isabelle and Jean-Pierre worked very hard for Monsieur Pompeux. No house in Paris was cleaner, no meals were tastier. But Monsieur Pompeux always found something to complain about.

"Isabelle, the picture frame has a spot on it!" he would say, or, "Jean-Pierre, this chicken needs more salt!"

To Jean-Pierre the kitchen was his whole world. With his many spoons and bowls, vegetables, cheeses, and eggs, he loved to create new and tasty dishes.

"How dare Monsieur Pompeux insult my cooking!" he cried. "Someday when I am a famous chef he will eat his words...but he will never eat my food!"

Isabelle, too, was tired of Monsieur Pompeux's complaints. She always cleaned every room in the house until it was spotless.

Every room, that is, except the locked room, which she was forbidden to enter. "Whatever is in that room must be filthy," she thought.

Once while Isabelle was polishing the doorknob to the locked room, she tried to peek through the keyhole. But Monsieur Pompeux caught her and he was furious. After that, he blocked up the keyhole and the door remained closed.

For Jean-Pierre and Isabelle the nicest part of the day was their free hour after Monsieur Pompeux's lunch. Then they bicycled to the River Seine.

After a stroll along the riverbank, they stopped at a café. Here they sat and talked about their dream to open a restaurant. They pictured how the restaurant would look and what they would serve.

They imagined Jean-Pierre as the master chef, accepting the praise of his happily stuffed customers.

Before they knew it, the hour slipped by. Jean-Pierre and Isabelle had to put their dreams aside and return to Monsieur Pompeux.

"Isabelle," cried Monsieur Pompeux one morning, "I must attend a business lunch this afternoon. I want you to stay in and mind the store!"

With that he rushed out, slamming the door behind him. Isabelle and Jean-Pierre peered gloomily out the window.

"No bicycle ride today," said Isabelle sadly.

"Don't worry," said Jean-Pierre, trying to be cheerful, "I'll cook a special lunch for us here." Off he went to the kitchen.

Alone in the store with nothing to do, Isabelle looked around and began to get an idea.

"I think I'll give these dirty antiques a good spring cleaning for a change," she decided. "Surely Monsieur Pompeux will smile for once in his grumpy life if he sees how shiny the store can look."

She set to work with rag and polish.

Soon the antiques began to glimmer brightly.
Just then one of Monsieur Pompeux's best customers, Madame
Tempête, came to browse.

As soon as she saw the polished antiques, she screamed: "Fakes, fakes! These are nothing but brass and tin!" Out the door, down the street ran Madame Tempête, yelling, "Fakes, fakes!"

Before Isabelle had time to realize what was happening, in rushed Monsieur Pompeux. He took one look at his sparkling objects and screamed: "What have you done?! I'm ruined!"

He was just about to bolt the door when in rushed Madame
Tempête and three gendarmes.

"Arrest him! He's a crook!" cried Madame Tempête.

"After him!" yelled the gendarmes. Monsieur Pompeux ran for
the stairs.

The gendarmes blew their whistles furiously...

as they all chased Monsieur Pompeux up the stairs and into the kitchen.

"O, la, la, there goes my lunch!" cried Jean-Pierre as Monsieur Pompeux crashed into the stove, knocking over the pot of soup. Madame Tempête slipped on the soup. The gendarmes landed on top of Madame Tempête. Dishes and cups crashed to the floor as Monsieur Pompeux crawled under the table and out the door.

"Mon Dieu, he's heading for the roof!" cried Isabelle. "Catch him, Jean-Pierre!"

"I won't let him get away!" called Jean-Pierre, and he led the chase up the winding staircase.

Puffing, panting, and grumbling, Monsieur Pompeux reached the door of the locked room. He was turning the key when…BOP!…down came Jean-Pierre's soup spoon on his head.

"Voilà, I've got him!" he cried as the door flew open and everyone burst into the room.

"Just as I thought," said Isabelle, "this room is filthy!" The studio was filled with cheap statues, paintings, musical instruments, and vases. Scattered about the table lay brushes, glue, and odd-colored paints used to make all the objects look old.

"It looks as if you've caught a famous antique forger," said the head gendarme to Jean-Pierre and Isabelle. And with that they marched Monsieur Pompeux off to jail.

Isabelle and Jean-Pierre were given
a large reward. The first thing that
they did with the money was to buy
Monsieur Pompeux's house and turn it
into a restaurant.

When the restaurant was ready to open, Jean-Pierre and Isabelle invited Madame Tempête and the three gendarmes to a specially prepared private dinner. They all drank a toast to the new restaurant and cried:

"Bon appétit!"

People still come to number seven, Rue Petite from all over. But now they don't come to bargain and buy antiques. They come to eat at "Chez Isabelle et Jean-Pierre." Afterward, the satisfied customers shout: "Bravo, Monsieur Jean-Pierre, compliments to the chef!"

It is by far the finest restaurant on either side of the Seine…
…"And the cleanest!" says Isabelle.